Mass for a New Century

a
congregational
setting

Andrew Moore

Kevin
Mayhew

We hope you enjoy *Mass for a New Century.* Further copies are available from your local music shop or Christian bookshop.

In case of difficulty, please contact the publisher direct by writing to:

The Sales Department
KEVIN MAYHEW LTD
Buxhall
Stowmarket
Suffolk IP14 3BW

Phone 01449 737978
Fax 01449 737834
E-mail info@kevinmayhewltd.com

Please ask for our complete catalogue of outstanding Church Music.

First published in Great Britain in 2000 by Kevin Mayhew Ltd.

© Copyright 2000 Kevin Mayhew Ltd.

ISBN 1 84003 528 5
ISMN M 57004 673 7
Catalogue No: 1400243

0 1 2 3 4 5 6 7 8 9

Cover design by Jonathan Stroulger

Music Setter: Donald Thomson
Proof-reader: Linda Ottewell

Printed and bound in Great Britain

Accompanying CD

Sally Thornton – soprano, Joyce Tindsley – alto,
Matthew Minter – tenor, Adrian Blakeley – bass
Recorded at St Margaret's Church, Prestwich, by Jon Blamire
Mixed at Sound Advice, Normanton, by Richard Lacy
Produced by Christopher Norton for CN Productions
Digital editing and mastering at The Loft, Huddersfield,
by Richard Kimmings

Musicians:
Simeon Wood – flute, Andrew Maries – oboe,
John Horton – organ
Conducted by Christopher Norton

Performance Notes

An optional instrumental part is provided throughout *Mass for a New Century*. This part is also given at the back of the book transcribed for B♭ instruments, as well as C instruments. If there is more than one instrument available, the instrumental part may be divided, as indicated by 1 and 2 above the instrumental stave.

The intercessions in the *Kyrie 2 (Penitential Rite)* may be sung, or said, in ordinary speech rhythm. Alternative intercessions may be used. The *Gloria* may be sung by everyone throughout, or responsorially.

The optional instrumental parts should remain tacet in the *Memorial Acclamation*.

MASS FOR A NEW CENTURY

Andrew Moore

KYRIE 1 (Penitential Rite)

Celebrant *mp*

Lord Jesus, you are mighty God and Prince of

Peace. Lord, have mer - cy.

All

Lord, have

mer - cy.

Celebrant
Lord Jesus, you are Son of God and Son of Ma - ry. Christ, have mer -

cy. Christ, have mer - cy.

All

Lord Jesus, you are Word made flesh and splendour of the Fa-ther. Lord, have mer - cy. Lord, have mer - cy.

KYRIE 2 (Penitential Rite)

mer - cy.

Celebrant or Cantor

Christ, have mer - cy.

All

Christ, have mer - cy.

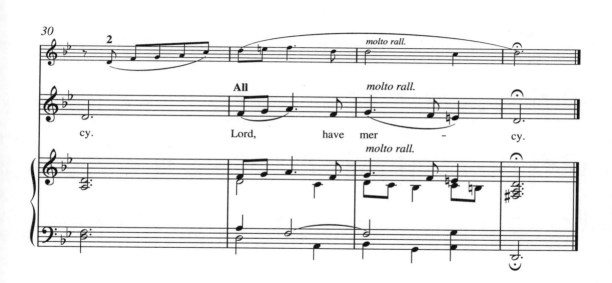

GLORIA

you take a-way the sin of the world, have mer-cy on us, have mer-cy on us.

You who sit at the Fa-ther's right hand, re - ceive our prayer, re - ceive our prayer.

Glo-ry to God in the high - est, glo-ry to God in the high - est,

glo-ry to God in the high - est, and peace to his peo-ple, his peo-ple on earth.

Verse 3

For you a-lone are the Ho-ly One, you a-lone are the Lord,

you a - lone are the Most High

Je - sus Christ, with the Ho - ly Spi - rit, in the glo - ry of God the Fa - ther.

Glo- ry to God in the high - est, glo- ry to God in the high - est,

glo - ry to God in the high - est, and peace to his peo - ple, his

peo-ple on earth. A - men, a - men, a - men, a - men.

SANCTUS

full of your glo - ry, ho - san - na, ho - san - na, ho - san - na in the

high - est, ho - san - na, ho - san - na, ho - san - na in the high - est.

Bles - sed is he who

Lyrics:
comes in the name of the Lord, bles-sed is he who
comes in the name of the Lord. Ho - san - na, ho - san - na, ho - san - na in the
high-est, ho - san - na, ho - san - na, ho - san - na in the high-est.

MEMORIAL ACCLAMATION

DOXOLOGY AND GREAT AMEN

Through him, with him, in him, in the u-ni-ty of the Ho - ly Spi - rit,

all glo-ry and ho-nour is yours, al-migh-ty Fa - ther, for e-ver and e - ver.

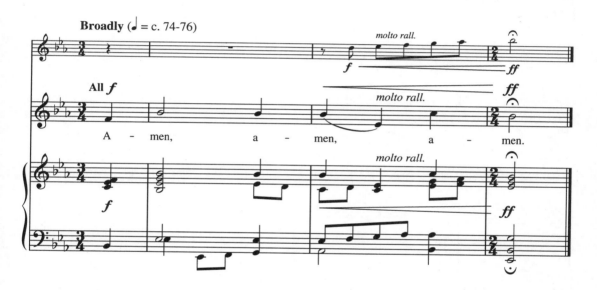

A - men, a - men, a - men.

AGNUS DEI

*1st time, instruments tacet or double the vocal melody

Lamb of God, Lamb of God, you take a - way the

sins of the world. Grant us, grant us your peace.

Please photocopy this page

KEVIN MAYHEW EASY COPYRIGHT CLEARANCE

The setting in this book is copyright and must not be reproduced in any way without the proper permission.

A one-year licence to reproduce the congregational part only of *Mass for a New Century* for non-commercial use may be obtained from the Kevin Mayhew Copyright Department by sending a copy of this page together with your payment.

Name of Church _____

Contact Name _____

Address _____

_____

Postcode _____

Telephone Number _____ Fax Number _____

E-mail _____

Fee for one-year licence: £10.58.

This fee is valid until 31 December 2002. After that date please contact the Copyright Department for information.

Please enclose payment by cheque or fill in the details of your Visa/Mastercard number below.

																	Expiry date until end _____

Signed _____

- -

To be completed by Kevin Mayhew Ltd

Payment of £10.58 received. Thank you.

Permission is granted subject to the following further conditions:

1. that the composer is acknowledged on every copy.

2. that the following copyright line is included on every copy:

> Copyright Kevin Mayhew Ltd. Reproduced by permission from *Mass for a New Century*

Licence Number _____ Licence expires on: _____

Signed for Kevin Mayhew Ltd _____

Copyright Department, Kevin Mayhew Ltd, Buxhall, Stowmarket, Suffolk, IP14 3BW
Telephone number: UK 01449 737978   International +44 1449 737978
Fax number: UK 01449 737834   International +44 1449 737834
E-mail: info@kevinmayhewltd.com

MASS FOR A NEW CENTURY

Congregation

Andrew Moore

GLORIA

At a good pace, but not too fast (♩. = c. 75)

52 are the Most High Je - sus Christ, with the Ho - ly Spi - rit, in the glo- ry of

56 *f Refrain*
God the Fa - ther. Glo- ry to God in the high - est, glo- ry to God in the

60 *rall.*
high - est, glo- ry to God in the high - est, and peace to his peo- ple, his

64 *rall.*
peo-ple on earth. A - men, a - men, a - men, a - men.

SANCTUS

Alla Marcia (♩ = c. 102-104)

8 **All** *f*
Ho-ly, ho- ly, ho - ly Lord, God of pow-er and

15 *cresc.* *f* *mf*
God of might. Hea-ven and earth are full of your glo- ry, ho - san-na, ho-

22 *cresc.*
san-na, ho - san-na in the high-est, ho - san-na, ho - san-na, ho - san-na in the

28 *f* 4 *mf*
high-est. Bles-sed is he who comes in the name of the Lord,

37 *più f* *mf*
bles-sed is he who comes in the name of the Lord. Ho - san-na, ho - san-na, ho-

43 *cresc.* *f*
san-na in the high-est, ho - san-na, ho - san-na, ho - san-na in the high-est.

29

MEMORIAL ACCLAMATION

Alla Marcia (♩ = c. 102-104)

Let us proclaim the my - ste - ry of faith. Christ has died.

Christ is ri - sen. Christ will come, will come a - gain.

Christ has died. Christ is ri - sen. Christ will come, will

come a - gain, Christ will come, will come a - gain.

DOXOLOGY AND GREAT AMEN

Through him, with him, in him, in the u - ni - ty of the Ho - ly Spi - rit,

all glo - ry and ho - nour is yours, al - migh - ty Fa - ther, for e - ver and e - ver.

Broadly (♩ = c. 74-76)

A - men, a - men, a - men.

AGNUS DEI

Gently (♩ = c. 78-80)

Lamb of God, Lamb of God, you

take a - way the sins of the world, have mer - cy,

have mer - cy on us. Lamb of God,

Lamb of God, you take a - way the

sins of the world. Grant us, grant us your peace.

MASS FOR A NEW CENTURY

Andrew Moore

KYRIE 1 (Penitential Rite)

KYRIE 2 (Penitential Rite)

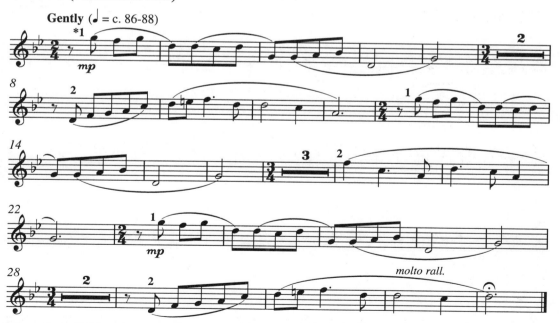

* Throughout this Mass, instrumental parts may be divided up between different players or instruments as indicated by the figures 1 and 2.

GLORIA

56 *Refrain*

62

SANCTUS

Alla Marcia (♩ = c. 102-104)

9

17

24

35

42

MEMORIAL ACCLAMATION
TACET

DOXOLOGY & GREAT AMEN

AGNUS DEI

* 1st time optional.

MASS FOR A NEW CENTURY

Andrew Moore

KYRIE 1 (Penitential Rite)

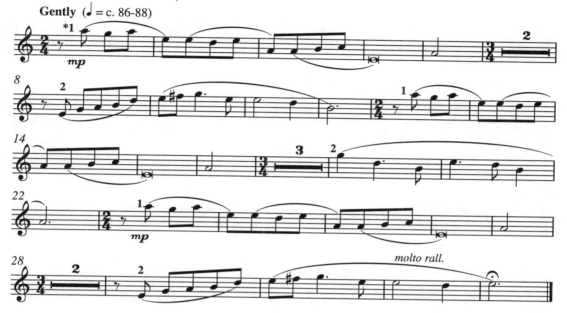

KYRIE 2 (Penitential Rite)

* *Throughout this Mass, instrumental parts may be divided up between different players or instruments as indicated by the figures 1 and 2.*

GLORIA

SANCTUS

MEMORIAL ACCLAMATION
TACET

DOXOLOGY & GREAT AMEN

AGNUS DEI

* 1st time optional.